S0-BYM-413

Simple Truths . . . Reimagined

ALPHABET LIVING

by
Dr. Bee & Hobo Dan

illustrated by
Dr. Bee

eXperience Open Unity Zest
Love Kindness Solitude Yearning Dreams Trust
Courage Nature Peace Authentic Joy Respect Music Beauty Humor
Exercise Gratitude Imagination Forgiveness Questioning Wisdom Voice

This alphabet provides to all
some simple truths for Being.
The Presence in each word
may swiftly spark new ways of seeing.

Inspired by: Julien

Special thanks to:

All of the people who helped to make this project a reality—
you know who you are!

Copyright © 2012 text and illustration / art: Rebecca Kovan, Ph.D.,
Daniel MacIntyre
All Rights Reserved.
Neither this book nor any part may be reproduced or transmitted in any form or by any means, electronic or mechanical,
including photocopying, microfilming, and recording, or by any information storage and retrieval system,
without written permission from the authors.

Book layout and graphic design by Rebecca Kovan, Ph.D. & Daniel MacIntyre
ALPHABET LIVING cover font—Coaster Shadow, by Dieter Steffman
initial concept art—acrylic on board, by C. O'Connell
Printed in the United States of America

1 2 3 4 5 6 7 8 9 10
♥
First Edition
Alphabet Living

ISBN: 978-0-615-38391-0

www.alphabetliving.com

THIS BOOK IS DEDICATED TO

LIFE

Authentic is a truthful way
to walk and talk and be.

Authentic shows the best of you
while living fearlessly.

For when you are Authentic
then you never have to doubt.

Authentic stands for being real—
that's what it's all about!

AUTHENTIC

B

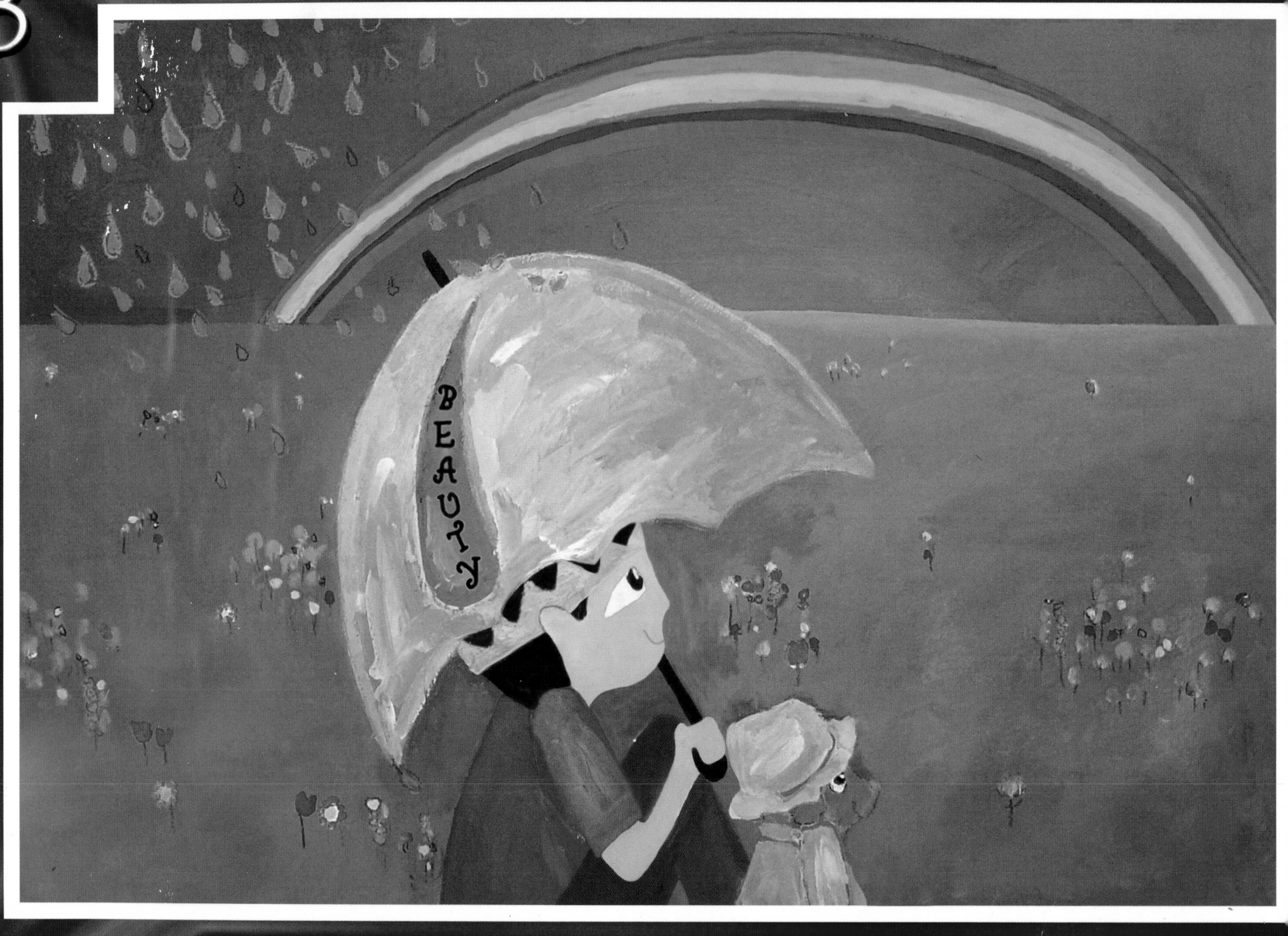

Beauty takes so many forms—
just simply look around.

Beauty is in nature
and in people's hearts it's found.

Go beyond the surface;
that's where Beauty fully flowers.

Beauty colors everything
with radiating powers!

BEAUTY

Courage is a quality of
bravery and strength.

Courage walks the hero's road—
it travels any length.

It's active drive wrapped up in bold
and pure determination.

Courage meets your challenges
with Being and elation!

COURAGE

Dreams are sacred hopes and plans
and wishes you hold dearly.

Dreams come true, you know they do,
just visualize them clearly.

Aim toward the sky and reach the stars—
your Dreams are fuel for flight.

Dreams that merge with thoughtfulness
will surely turn out right!

D
R
E
A
M
S

E

Exercise is healthy movement
for your WHOLE self's sake.

Exercise will keep you fit—
the fun is yours to make.

Well Being is the sense you gain
and energy is sprightly.

Exercise exhilarates;
you're bound to shine more brightly!

EXERCISE

Forgiveness is a path that heals—
it's good to let things go.

Forgiveness means you don't hold on;
this lets you greet Life's flow.

Transform your thoughts.
Forgiveness is the key
to rise above.

Forgiveness opens many doors,
especially to love.

FORGIVENESS

Gratitude is thankfulness—
complete appreciation

Gratitude is honoring
with graceful exclamation!

It's conscious praise for blessings
that have touched your Life somehow.

Gratitude acknowledges
the richness of right Now.

GRATITUDE

H

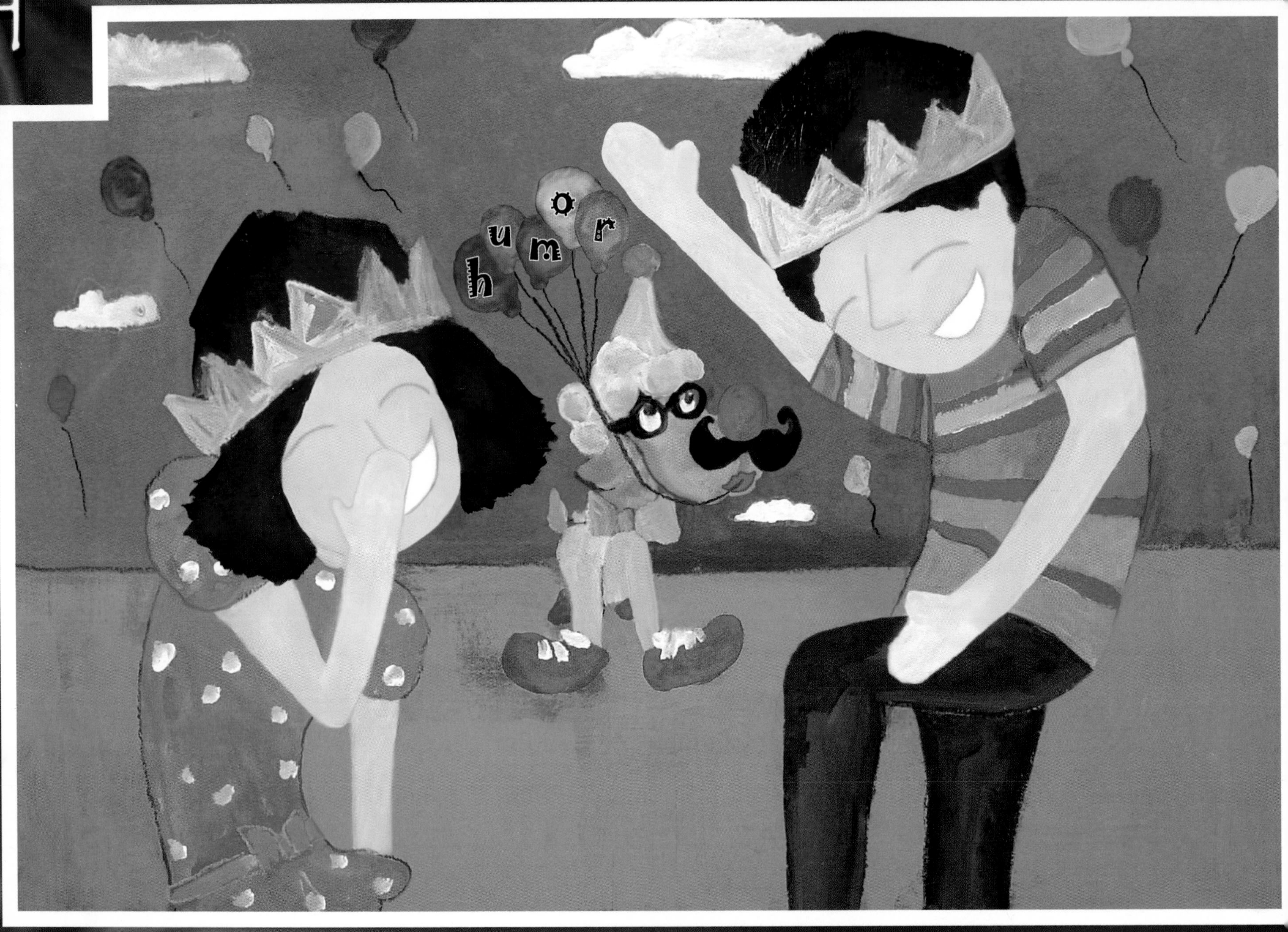

Humor triggers laughter,
which erupts
when something's funny.

Humor lifts your spirits,
and it turns the dark spots sunny.

Feeling sad or blue?
You'll find that Humor is a cure.

Humor tickles liveliness—
of this you can be sure!

HUMOR

Imagination activates
the rainbows of Creation.

Imagination journeys past
the place of limitation.

Nurture your Imagination—
it will take you higher.

Imagination blooms
with your attention and desire!

IMAGINATION

Joy is inspiration in your core—
it's sweet delight.

Joy is cheerful with a boost,
alive and out of sight.

With Joy in your midst,
you're filled with
health and wealth and healing.

Joy is splendid, dazzling,
brilliant, awesome, and appealing!

J
O
Y

Kindness is a gesture
reaching out to lend a hand.

Kindness is essential
to a happiness that's grand.

Try to treat all living things
with Kindness and a smile.

Kindness swells your heart
because you go the extra mile.

K
I
N
D
N
E
S
S

Love is what you feel
when you truly, deeply care.

Love can make your tummy flip—
it urges you to share.

Call upon the field of Love
should times get harsh or tough.

Love can make the difference,
for its power is enough!

L
O
V
E

M

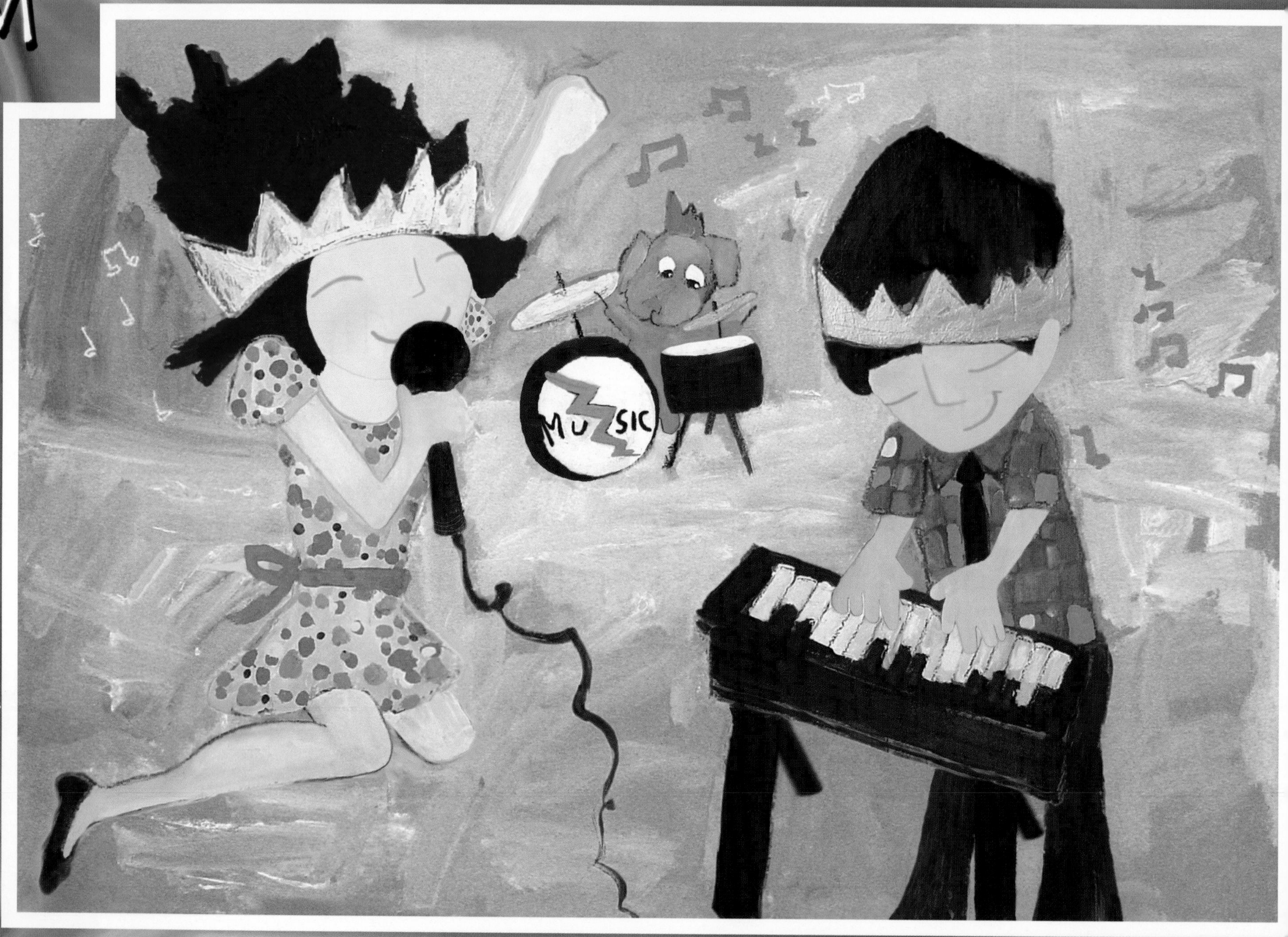

Music is a string of notes,
it's rhythm, and it's song.

Music resonates within,
inviting—
all belong.

Sing and dance, clap and play;
it's magic for your soul.

Music dwells in many sounds . . .
expand, then rock and roll!

MUSIC

Nature is the great outdoors—
embrace its realm of wonder!

Nature lives through animals,
all plants, and things like thunder.

Water, fire, air, and earth
are Nature's sacred four.

Nature gives you mysteries
and landscapes to explore.

NATURE

Open means available
and ready to receive.

Open is alert, where Being
has a chance to breathe.

It's tolerance for differences
that others may reveal.

Open shifts your mindset—
it's refreshing and ideal!

O
P
E
N

Peace is calming harmony
with all of your relations.

Peace is found when there exists
no fighting between nations.

To have a world that's conflict-free,
with Peace,
should be the goal.

Peace that starts within
improves the planetary whole!

P
E
A
C
E

Questioning ignites the flame
of shared investigation.

Questioning evolves ideas,
birthing innovation.

Should you not be sure
in which direction
you are leaning,

Questioning might point to . . .
"Find a path with heart and meaning!"

Respect is Presence
with another's
values, thoughts, and needs.

Respect is earned and fostered
through the merit of your deeds.

In meaningful relationships
Respect is sure required.

Respect yourself and you will see
your choices are inspired!

R
E
S
P
E
C
T

Solitude is quiet time
that simply lets you be.

Solitude provides a space
to revel in carefree.

If you need perspective
or must make a hard decision,

Solitude will help your cause
and clarify your vision!

SOLITUDE

Trust is cultivated by the way
you act and speak.

Trust promotes an essence
that is loyal and unique.

It's a key ingredient
in all of your connections.

Trust assures that you can show
your wholehearted affections!

T
R
U
S
T

Unity brings harmony
and kind cooperation.

Unity in people
is a cause for celebration.

Teamwork leads to Unity
by giving your assistance.

Unity is Oneness—
that's the well of your existence!

UNITY

Voice conveys belief and choice
with pitch, and tone, and sound.

Voice is what you use to sing—
your soul will glow all 'round!

So flex your Voice, affirm yourself,
and state your point of view.

Voice that has compassion
will reflect a better you.

Wisdom is insightful understanding
gained through time.

Wisdom has a quiet strength,
both humble and sublime.

Knowing that the moment's Now
is part of Wisdom's face.

Wisdom guides awareness
and perception into place!

eXperience creates a
woven fabric for your story.

eXperience contributes to
your own exclusive glory!

Adventure, friends, and loved ones
are support for its foundation.

eXperience occurs through
your sincere participation.

eXPERIENCE

Yearning is a private feeling
dwelling deep inside.

Yearning often tugs your heart—
much like an ocean's tide.

It's passion with a spirit
for connection to the Source.

Yearning in the Universe
builds influential force!

Zest involves a thirst for Life
that tingles on your skin.

Zest attracts excitement with pizzazz—
one two three . . . grin!

It's flair, it's style,
it's joie de vivre*, it's gusto.
"Welcome Zest!"

Zest invigorates with charm—
that's thrilling and the best.

* joy of life

Z
E
S
T

* Poem from A - Z *

AUTHENTIC through and through enlightens

BEAUTY that you see.

COURAGE in your Being shapes grand

DREAMS of victory!

EXERCISE improves your health and makes you really strong.

FORGIVENESS keeps your spirit light when letting go of wrong.

GRATITUDE is genuine and leads to further blessings.

HUMOR spices up each day's

IMAGINATION dressings!

JOY elicits

KINDNESS, which in turn, elicits

LOVE.

MUSIC is in

NATURE, both below and up above!

OPEN hearts bring

PEACE world 'round, where

QUESTIONING is treasured.

RESPECT the time for

SOLITUDE—its value can't be measured.

TRUST supports a tranquil Earth, with

UNITY prevailing.

VOICE will get your point across, and

WISDOM sets you sailing!

eXPERIENCE the wonder that's for you to seek and find, while

YEARNING for pure loveliness bestowed upon Allkind.

ZEST each day will make the moments great, both big and small . . .

Hobo Dan has one more vital
thing he'd like to say,

before you turn this final page
and move on with your day.

The message is important
and he feels that you should know . . .

YOU HAVE A CHOICE

TAKE WHAT WORKS

LET EVERYTHING ELSE GO

authentic
beauty
courage
dreams
exercise
forgiveness
gratitude
humor
imagination
joy
kindness
love
music
nature
open
peace
questioning
respect
solitude
trust
unity
voice
wisdom
experience
yearning
zest

thank you for reading me

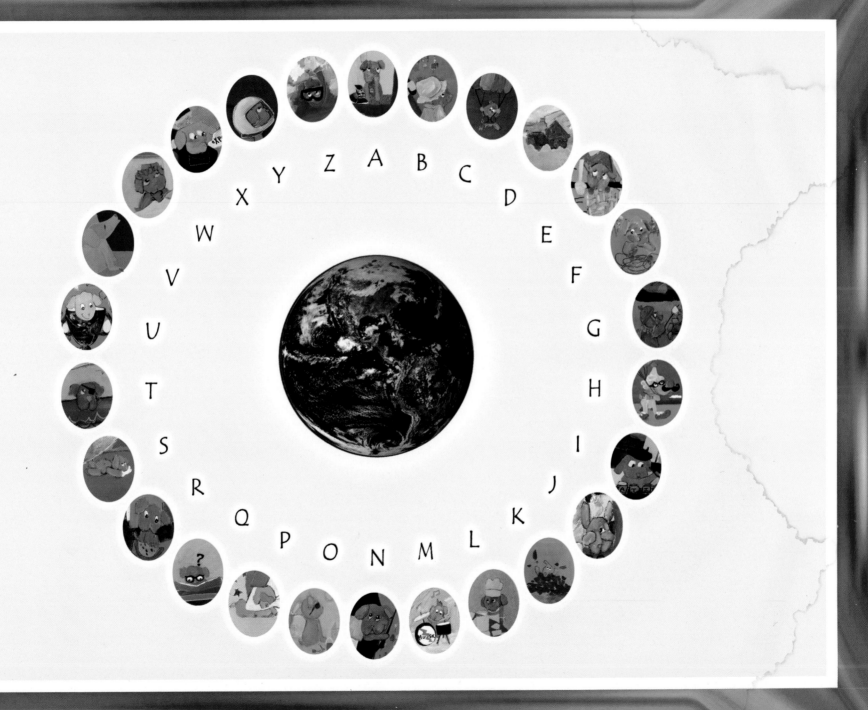